MUSICAL MOMENTS

Clarinet

Book 1

16 original compositions
& arrangements
for Clarinet & Piano

Selected and edited by
Kirsty Hetherington

Published by
Trinity College London

Registered Office:
89 Albert Embankment
London SE1 7TP UK

T +44 (0)20 7820 6100
F +44 (0)20 7820 6161
E music@trinitycollege.co.uk
www.trinitycollege.co.uk

Registered in the UK
Company no. 02683033
Charity no. 1014792

Layout: Moira Roach/Scott Barnard

Printed in England by Halstan & Co. Ltd, Amersham, Bucks.

Lefty ho!

With character ♩ = 126

Sarah Watts

Gavotte

arr. Andrew Challinger

Jean-Baptiste Loeillet de Gant
(1688–c. 1720)

Moderato ♩ = c. 120

2

No New Messages

Sarah Watts

Rožek

from *Moravian Dances* JW VI/7

arr. David Adlam

Leoš Janáček
(1854-1928)

The Dinosaurs are Dancing

Spiritosaurus ♩ = 120

Paul Harris

The Harp That Once Through Tara's Halls

arr. Gareth McLearnon

Traditional Irish

Andante ♩ = c. 80

True Love

(Swabian Air)

arr. Patrick Gundry-White

Traditional German

Dr Hugh's Medicinal Rag

James Rae
(born 1957)

Andantino

from Sonatina in C, op. 15 no. 2

arr. David Adlam

Anton Diabelli
(1781–1858)

I Was Doing All Right

arr. Andreas Panayi

George Gershwin
(1898–1937)

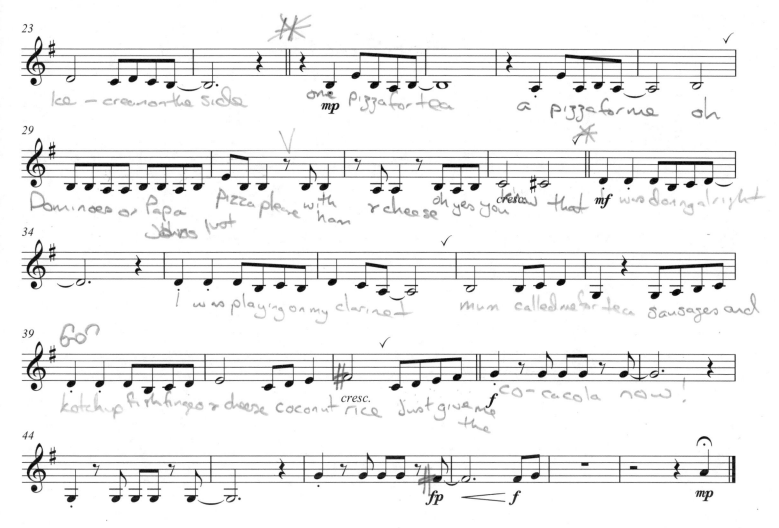

Menuett 1

from *Music for the Royal Fireworks* HWV 351

arr. Robin Hagues

George Frideric Handel
(1685-1759)

Panis Angelicus

arr. Andrew Challinger

César Franck
(1822–1890)

Waltz at Midnight

Paul Harris

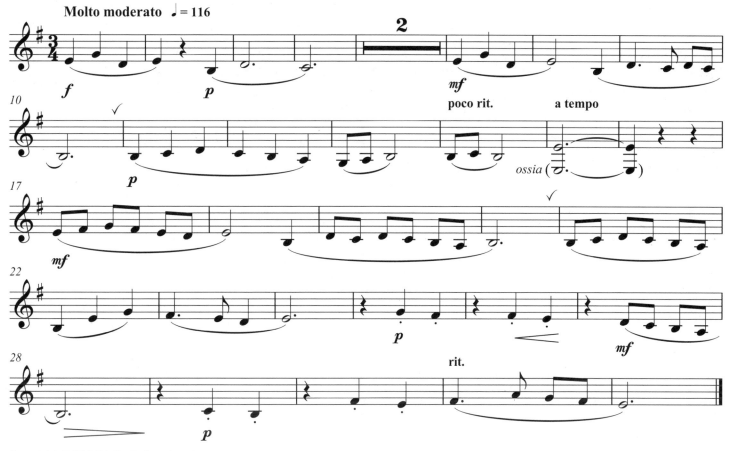

Melody
from *Album for the Young* op. 68

arr. Patrick Gundry-White

Robert Schumann
(1810-1856)

English Country Gardens

arr. John DeHolt

After the Snow

James Rae
(born 1957)

10